The Young Vic Theatre Company

presents

The Nativity

adapted and directed by
David Farr

The Young Vic is supported by

YOUNG VIC

The Young Vic Theatre Company brings new versions of classic stories and great plays to audiences of all ages and backgrounds. Committed to making theatre available to all, particularly the young, we cultivate new audiences and integrate our productions with extensive off-stage work with partners in education and the community.

Teaching others about theatre, and learning ourselves from this activity, is integral to the Young Vic. We provide young people with the practical means to explore theatre through the skills and experience of our award-winning core creative team.

In recognition of our national and international reputation, we take our work beyond this theatre to audiences throughout Britain and across the world. We invite other leading theatre companies, who share our approaches to theatre, to bring their work to audiences at the Young Vic.

THE YOUNG VIC THEATRES
Main House

The main auditorium at the Young Vic is one of London's most adaptable spaces. It is used to great effect to house a wide range of new works by outstanding artists: from magical adaptations of stories such as *Arabian Nights* and *Grimm Tales* to uncompromising new versions of Genet and Shakespeare.

The performance arenas of Ancient Greece and Rome originally inspired its design seating up to 500 people. Performances are given in-the-round, thrust, traverse or in fact any number of variations, and the unique nature of the auditorium means that the audience is never far from the stage, able to enjoy an intimate view of the action.

To allow us to use the main auditorium as flexibly as possible, we have unreserved seating which lets us position the audience in the best possible relationship to the stage area. We do not actually confirm our maximum seating capacity until the first preview performance, thus further enabling the seating configuration to be adapted in direct response to developments in on-stage rehearsals. It would not be possible to introduce reserved seating and maintain this distinctive flexibility of the auditorium. We hope that each time you enter the Young Vic Theatre you are pleasantly surprised by our inventive set designs and stage configurations.

Young Vic Studio

The Young Vic Studio is one of London's most important homes of experimental new theatre. Leading companies present work that subverts, questions and reflects contemporary life. Seating up to 80 people, it is similarly flexible in configuration to the main auditorium. If you come and see a show in the Studio theatre you could find yourself sitting in-the-round, along one side, in the middle or even walking about as the performance takes place around you.

YOUNG VIC – FUNDING AND INCOME

The Young receives annual funding from the Arts Council of England, London Arts Board, the London Boroughs Grant Committee and Lambeth and Southwark Councils. These grants represent 37% of annual income. A further 4% is realised through fund raising and donations. The remaining 59% is dependent on income generated through the Box Office (which is itself entirely based upon the success of individual productions throughout the year), theatre hires and programme sales. The volatility of income generated through the Box Office has an immediate effect on our planning and, as a non-commercial theatre, we must constantly balance our artistic mission against this financial reality.

In the last 12 months over 95,000 people have attended performances at the Young Vic, we have worked with over 3,000 young people in London's inner-city communities and over 10,000 people have experienced the magic of live theatre (many for the first time) through our Funded Ticket Scheme.

The Young Vic's annual programme of work, including 5 productions annually, national and international touring, theatre workshops, the Funded Ticket Scheme, building maintenance and other overheads costs approximately £2m.

The actors in the production you are watching are all paid Equity minimum salaries, and all other members of the creative and support team, as well as permanent administrative staff, receive salaries on a similar scale. The strain on our resources unfortunately means that issues like under-investment in the fabric of the building (from the cramped foyer to insufficient toilets to poor backstage facilities) is not a choice, but a simple reality. We must use our resources to create the work we have become renowned for, and are currently pursuing strategies to realise additional resources to develop the theatre building and secure the future of the Young Vic.

GET INVOLVED – TEACHING, PARTICIPATION AND RESEARCH

From doing workshops with actors and directors, to attending performances for free or even working on your own production, the Young Vic Theatre Company offers a range of ways to get involved in theatre and support our work.

We provide young people from 3 to 20 years old with the practical means to explore theatre through the skills and experience of our award-winning core creative team. This process of research directly informs our work on stage.

Our programme includes: theatre making activities; music, text, voice and body teaching projects; on-stage production workshops; a Schools' Theatre Festival; written resource material; workshops both with studio practitioners; and for young professionals, an extensive work experience and apprenticeship programme.

All the work is free of charge to participants and runs in tandem with the Funded Ticket Scheme that offers access to performances through free or highly subsidised tickets. Currently our activities primarily focus on the London inner city boroughs of Lambeth and Southwark with the expectation of developing links with other South East London Boroughs.

For more information, please write to:
TPR, Young Vic, 66 The Cut, London SE1 8LZ.

ARTS FOR EVERYONE

In September 1997, the Young Vic was awarded one of the highest National Lottery Arts for Everyone (A4E) awards in the country. This three year award has enabled us to better resource and realise our core activities, which are crucial to the Young Vic's continued development. Some of these core activities are:

- The growth of the Young Vic's Funded Ticket Scheme, which is one of the largest audience development access projects in the country.

- The encouragement of young artists on the cutting edge of performance to develop their work through experimentation in the Young Vic's award-winning Studio.

- A substantial and significant increase in the Young Vic's acclaimed work with teachers, schools, colleges and young people.

- More adequate resources for Young Vic Productions, which has enabled us to bring to the stage outstanding productions by some of Britain's leading talents.

In order to realise the enormous potential of this award, the Young Vic has been finding companies, trusts and individuals that share a commitment to the work we undertake each year. Over the three years of the grant award, the Young Vic must raise a total of £100,000 in partnership funding from these sources in order to release this additional funding.

The additional A4E funding towards our core activities will cease in 2001. We are currently devising strategies to try and replace the £130,000 per year that this represents in order to ensure the artistic and financial success of recent years can continue.

AUDIENCE DEVELOPMENT
THE YOUNG VIC FUNDED TICKET SCHEME

The Young Vic Funded Ticket Scheme (main sponsor Allied Domecq plc) provides an introduction to theatre for thousands of people from all social and economic backgrounds who might not have considered a trip to see live theatre. Initially created in 1994 to enable local school children, based on need, to visit the theatre for the first time, the scheme has been radically expanded due to a successful application to the National Lottery's Art's for Everyone programme.

The expanded Funded Ticket Scheme, now in it's second year, brought close to 10,000 new theatregoers to the Young Vic during year one. If you would like further information on how a group from your place of work or organisation within London or the home counties can become involved, please call the Audience Develoment Department on 0207 633 0133.

BECOME A PART OF THE FUTURE OF BRITISH THEATRE

If you have enjoyed this performance of *The Nativity* why not become a Friend of the Young Vic and enjoy a wealth of special Friends' activities and behind-the-scenes glimpses of the varied work of the Young Vic – regarded by many as the future of British theatre.

Above all, your support will help us to maintain our position as a leading centre for theatre which embraces people of all ages and backgrounds.

The Young Vic takes this opportunity to express its particular thanks to those who have kindly agreed to support our work at the following levels of support:

Patron

Mr C J Bates
Lou Coulson
Jeremy Drax
Clare Garvin
Dr and Mrs Herzberg
Lady Lever
Terence Pentony
Andy Stinson
Diane Sundt
The Tracy Family
Gerry Wade and Robert Hasty
Rebecca Wennington-Ingram

Katie Bradford
Ruth Downing
Jennifer Gubbins
The Kings School, Canterbury
Patrick McKenna
Dr Martin Smith
Jan Topham
Val Gilbert Ltd
Sybella Zisman

Benefactor

Norma Acland
Gillian Diamond
R F P Hardman
Lew Hodges
Anya Jones
Stuart and Julie Maister
David and Anthea Minnet
Dr Oppenheimer
C Polemis
Murray Shanks
Mr M Graham-Smith
Janet Walker
Mr and Mrs George White

David Day
Michael Greenhalgh
Sheila Harvey
Joanna Howard
Victoria Neumark Jones
Mina Martinez
Barbara Minto
Mrs G M C Phillips
Barbara Poole
Mr K H Simmonds
Ann and Peter Snow
Anthony Watkinson
Penny Whitson

Christina Burton
Allegra Castellini
Jessica Fenton
Trevor Parsons
Nick Pizey
Anthony Salz
Richard Slater
David Van Oss
Anda Winters
Paula Clement
Jean Elliott
Bruce & Clare Johnson
Richard Price Television Ltd.
Carmi Weinzweig

Our thanks, too, to our many Friends who have kindly joined at the Supporter and Contributor levels and, of course, our many Young Friends.

For further information on becoming a Friend of the Young Vic please take a leaflet from the display in the foyer or contact the Young Vic Development Office on **0171 633 0133.**

The Young Vic Theatre Company presents

The Nativity

Performers	*in alphabetical order*
Sarah Theresa Belcher	**Caspar**
Dave Fishley	**Abraham**
Kate Fleetwood	**Balthazar**
Toby Jones	**Joseph**
Dominic McHale	**Benjamin**
Sabina Netherclift	**Melchior**
Toby Sedgwick	**Herod**
Nicholas Sidi	**The Devil**
Nina Sosanya	**Mary**

Other parts played by	members of the company

Adapted and directed by	**David Farr**
Designed by	**Angela Davies**
Music by	**Paul Clark**
Lighting by	**Adam Silverman**
Puppetry director	**Sue Buckmaster**
Sound by	**Crispian Covell**
Script Editor	**Simon Reade**
Musical instruments by	**David Sawyer**
Illusions by	**Paul Kieve**
Music Coach	**James Keane**
Assistant Director	**Craig Higginson**
Company Stage Manager	**Clare McCaffrey**
Deputy Stage Managers	**Clare Norwood**
	Jack Morrison

*First performed at
the Young Vic Theatre on* **22 November 1999**

BIOGRAPHIES

SARAH THERESA BELCHER *Caspar*
Theatre includes: for The Wrestling School – *The Ecstatic Bible* (Barbican), *He Stumbled* (Almeida), *Ursula* (National Tour). Other theatre work includes *Stranded* (Scarlet Theatre – Young Vic Studio), *A River Sutra* (RNT Studio co-production – Three Mills Island Studio), *The Ballad of Wolves*, *Candide*, *Leonce and Lena* (all Gate Theatre), *Metamorphoses*, *The Silver Swan* (all Clod Ensemble), *Sunspots* (The Red Room). Television includes *Vanity Fair* (Latenight Pictures), Amelia's Songs (BBC).

SUE BUCKMASTER *Puppetry Director*
As Co-Artistic Director of Theatre-rites, work includes *Houseworks* (Out of Lift), *Millworks* (Greenwich and Docklands Festival), *Cellarworks* (Lift 1999) and *The Lost and Moated Land* (tour, including the Young Vic Studio). Other work as Puppetry Director includes *The Caucasian Chalk Circle* (Theatre de Complicite), *Bartholomew Fair* (RSC), Julia Bardsley's *Hamlet?* (Young Vic), Phelim McDermott's *The Ghost Downstairs* (Leicester Haymarket), and work for Tara Arts, Nottingham Roundabout and Pop-Up Theatre. Recent work includes a performance to open this year's British Festival of Visual Theatre at BAC, and future projects include a new performance for the Unicorn Children's Theatre.

PAUL CLARK *Composer*
Theatre includes *Lady Grey* (Clod Ensemble/Purcell Room), *It's a Small House* (Clod Ensemble/Split Britches), *The Silver Swan*, *The Overcoat*, *Metamorphoses*, *The Feast During the Plague* (all Clod Ensemble), *Poor Mrs Pepys* (Red Shift), *A Dark River* (The Big Picture Co.). Films include *Esther Khan* (Why Not/Zephyr), *Roubles* (BBC2), *Glow Boys* (BFI).

CRISPIAN COVELL *Sound Designer*
After training at the Guildhall School of Music and Drama, Crispian joined Cirque du Soleil's sound department on their tour of Algeria. After returning to the UK, he continued freelancing for Orbital, B&H, Autograph and other sound companies. Projects include *Kat and the Kings* (Capital Live Entertainment – European Tour), *Happy Days, The Musical* (E&B Productions – UK Tour), programming cruise ship shows for Carnivale Cruises (West Indies and New York), parties for UCI Films, *Swan Lake* (English National Ballet – Arena Tour), *Nina Simone in Concert* and The Church of England's Lambeth Conference, 1998. Work as sound designer includes *Arabian Nights* (Young Vic UK Tour), *The Jewess of Toledo* (Bridewell Theatre), *King Lear* (Indian Summer Theatre Company Indian Tour), *Fantastic Mr Fox*, *The Snow Queen*, *Wind in the Willows* (MCN Productions), *Cabaret* (Guildhall Drama School).

ANGELA DAVIES *Designer*
Theatre includes *The House of Bernarda Alba* (Shared Experience), *Shadows* (RSC Touring), *The Maids Tragedy* (Shakespeare's Globe), *As You Like It* (Washington DC, Shakespeare Theatre Company), *Don Juan, The Hypochondriac* (both West Yorkshire Playhouse), *The Ballad of Wolves, The Portuguese Boat Plays, The Great Highway* (all Gate Theatre). Opera includes *Broken Strings* (Almeida Opera Festival). Films include *Simon Magus* (Channel Four). Future theatre work includes *Mother Courage* (Shared Experience), *The Insect Play* (Young Vic).

DAVID FARR *Adaptation/Director*
David Farr is a writer and director. As director he has focused on international work, and was Artistic Director of London's Gate Theatre from 1995-1998. Plays directed include *Seven Doors, The Great Highway, The Boat Plays, The Barbarous Comedies, Candide, Danton's Death* and *Leonce and Lena*. His own play *Elton John's Glasses* premiered at Watford in 1997 and won the Writer's Guild Best New Play of that season, opening in the West End in 1998. He has also directed two operas for Almeida Opera including Thomas Ades' *Powder Her Face*. He is currently under commission from the RSC and from the First Film Company.

DAVE FISHLEY *Abraham*
Theatre includes *Twelfth Night* (Nuffield Theatre), *The Other War* (West Yorkshire Playhouse), *Marat/Sade* (Royal National Theatre), *Ballad of Wolves, Silverface* (both Gate Theatre), *Now You Know* (Hampstead Theatre), *Asylum! Asylum!* (Abbey Theatre, Dublin), *Smoke* (Royal Exchange Theatre, Manchester), *Coloured Sands, Jimmy Jazz* (Changinspeak). Television includes *Macbeth* (BBC), *Touch of Frost* (Excelsior). Films includes *If Only, The Fifth Element, Collection, Coming Through Slaughter*.

KATE FLEETWOOD *Balthazar*
Theatre includes *Ghosts* (Theatre Royal Plymouth), *Arabian Nights* (Young Vic), *Romeo and Juliet* (Greenwich Theatre), *Swaggers* (The Old Red Lion), *Twelfth Night, Comic Mysteries, Love is a Drug* (all Oxford Stage Company). Television includes *Lizzie's Pictures* (BBC1), *Seriously Funny* (Channel Four), *Getting Hurt* (BBC Screen 2). Radio includes *Ruslan and Lyudmilla* (BBC).

CRAIG HIGGINSON *Assistant Director*
Craig is a writer and freelance dramaturg. Previous shows at the Young Vic as Assistant Director include *More Grimm Tales, Twelfth Night* and *As I Lay Dying*.

TOBY JONES *Joseph*
Theatre includes *A Midsummer Night's Dream* (Almeida/tour), *The Weavers* (Gate Theatre), *The Government Inspector* (West Yorkshire Playhouse), *King Lear* (West Yorkshire Playhouse/Hackney Empire),

Out of the House Walked a Man (Royal National Theatre/Theatre de Complicite, *Bitching, Booze and Bumming Fags* (writer and performer – BAC/British Festival of Visual Theatre). Television includes *The Aristocrats, Out of Hours, Henry IV, Death of a Salesman* (all BBC), *Midsomer Murders* (ITV). Films include *Hotel Splendide, Jeanne d'Arc, Simon Magus, Ever After, Les Miserables*.

JAMES KEANE *Music Coach*
Work includes: Conducting – *Vanity Fair* (BBC), *Ester Khan* (Magic Lantern Films), *Feast During the Plague, Musical Scenes, Metamorphoses, Pierrot Lunaire, The Silver Swan* (all Clod Ensemble). Orchestration – *Vanity Fair* (BBC), *Love in the Twenty-First Century* (Channel Four), *Fifty Revolutions* (Oxford Stage Company), *Sportarama* (The Cholmondeleys and The Featherstonehaughs). As instrumentalist – *Mojo* (Jez Butterworth), *Queer as Folk* (Channel Four), *The Overcoat* (Clod Ensemble), *Othello Music* (The Walking Orchestra). James was also an angel in Deborah Warner's *Tower Project* (LIFT).

PAUL KIEVE *Illusionist*
Theatre includes *The Invisible Man* (Theatre Royal Stratford East and West End), *Scrooge – The Musical* (Dominion Theatre/UK and International tours), *The Witches* (West End and tour – currently playing at Birmingham Old Rep), *The Strange Case of Dr Jekyll and Mr Hyde, The Mysteries, Spring Awakening* (all RSC), *La Grande Magia, Haroun and the Sea of Stories* (both RNT), *Arabian Nights* (Young Vic and current UK tour), *Angela Carter Cinderella* (Lyric Hammersmith), *Peter Pan* (West Yorkshire Playhouse). Ballet includes *Alice in Wonderland* (English National Ballet – Coliseum and UK tour). Opera includes *Macbeth* (Hamburg). Other work includes *Maze of Mirrors* (collaboration with Andrew Lloyd Webber – Sydmonton Festival), *The Magic of David Copperfield* (television – USA). As a performer, international appearances include *The Magic Castle*, Hollywood. Current work includes *Dick Whittington* (Sadler's Wells), *Peter Pan* (Copenhagen). Paul is a Gold Star member of the Inner Magic Circle.

DOMINIC McHALE *Benjamin*
Theatre includes *Oh What a Lovely War, Peter Pan* (both Royal National Theatre), *The Trial, The Tempest, Tell Me, Hansel and Gretel* (all Contact Theatre), *Hamlet, Strangers on a Train, Second From Last in the Sack Race* (all Chester Gateway), *The Fancy Man* (Hampstead Theatre), *Body 115* (Library Theatre). Television includes *Parallel Nine* (BBC1), *Coronation Street* (Granada), *Hope I Die Before I Get Old* (BBC2). Films include *The Short Walk* (Crucial/Channel 4).

SABINA NETHERCLIFT *Melchior*
Theatre includes *The Silver Swan, The Overcoat, Metamorphoses, Musical Scenes, The Feast During the Plague* (all Clod Ensemble), *The Suppliants, The Ballad of Wolves, Silverface* (all Gate Theatre),

Desire Caught by the Tail (Half-Baked Venus), *One Last Surviving* (Lyric Studio). Work as narrator includes *ABC/123* (Early Learning Centre), *Literary Landscapes* (Cameo Productions).

TOBY SEDGWICK *Herod*
Founder member of **The Moving Picture Mime Show**. Theatre includes *Help I'm Alive* (Theatre de Complicite), *Out of a House Walked a Man* (Theatre de Complicite/Royal National Theatre), *Wiseguy Scapino* (Theatr Clwyd), *The Servant of Two Masters* (West Yorkshire Playhouse), Harpo Marx in *Animal Crackers* (Royal Exchange Manchester and Lyric, West End). Work as Movement Director includes *Rosencrantz and Guildenstern Are Dead*, *Marat/Sade* (both Royal National Theatre), *Bartholomew Fair*, *Everyman* (both Royal Shakespeare Company), *Peek-a-Boo* and *Face to Face* (Souxsie and the Banshees). Television includes *Arena – Moving Picture Mime Show* (BBC2), *Museum of Madness – Ken Campbell* (Channel Four), *Monster Café*, *Hububb* (both BBC1). Work as director includes *George Dandin* (Redshift), *The Three Musketeers* (Mimetheatre Project).

NICHOLAS SIDI *The Devil*
Theatre includes *The Colonel Bird* (Gate Theatre), *Hustlers and Ashes to Ashes* (Royal Court), *Car* (Riverside Studios), *She's Electric* (Belgrade Theatre, Coventry), *Poe Play* (One Man Show – Etcetera Theatre), *Diary of a Madman* (Etcetera Theatre), *Much Ado About Nothing* (Tour). Television includes *This Life*, *No Sweat*, *City Central* (all BBC), *Coronation Street*, *Cold Feet*, *Passion Killers* (all Granada). Films include *Jesus* (Lobe Productions/CBS).

ADAM SILVERMAN *Lighting Designer*
Theatre includes *The Cider House Rules*, *Power Plays*, *The New Bozena* (all Off-Broadway, NYC), *Bartholomew Fair* (RSC), *Beauty and the Beast* (Young Vic and tour to New Zealand International Arts Festival), *A Tale of Two Cities*, *Cyrano de Bergerac* (both Gate Theatre, Dublin), *Hamlet* (Young Vic and tour to Japan), *'Tis Pity She's a Whore* (Young Vic). Opera includes *La Traviata* (New Israeli Opera and Houston Grand Opera), *Der Rosenkavalier* (Seattle Opera), *Cavalleria Rusticana* and *Pagliacci*, *Die Fledermaus*, *Eugene Onegin*, *The Merry Widow* (all Opera Ireland), *Faust* (Welsh National Opera).

NINA SOSANYA *Mary*
Theatre includes *Deadmeat* (West Yorkshire Playhouse), *Antony and Cleopatra* (Royal National Theatre), *The Tempest* (Teatro Botanicum), *The Herbal Bed*, *Henry V*, *The White Devil*, *The Learned Ladies* (all RSC), *The Tempest*, *Twelfth Night*, *A Midsummer Night's Dream* (all Oddsocks Theatre Company), *Dinner Dance* (The Kosh), *Hair* (Broadway Musical Theatre Company). Television includes *Jonathan Creek III* (BBC), *Hercules and the Amazon Women* (Renaissance Productions), *The Bill* (Carlton).

**The Young Vic would like to express its sincere thanks
to the many companies, foundations and
private contributors who recognise the value
of the company's work. These include:**

Abbey National Charitable Trust Limited, Allied Domecq plc,
Ambrose and Ann Appelbe Trust, The Avenue Charitable Trust,
Barclays Bank plc, Barclays Life Assurance Company Ltd, Bass plc,
Beechdean Dairies Ltd, Thomas Bendhem, The Berkeley Group plc,
British Steel plc, Calouste Gulbenkian Foundation, Carlton Television Trust,
The Coutts Charitable Trust, David Cohen Family Charitable Trust,
The Muriel and Gershon Coren Charitable Foundation,
The D'Oyly Carte Charitable Trust, David S Smith Holdings plc,
The Eric Evans Memorial Trust, Evening Standard, Frogmore Estates plc,
The Robert Gavron Charitable Trust, The Worshipful Company of Grocers,
The Guardian Royal Exchange Charitable Trust,
Mrs Margaret Guido's Charitable Trust, The Haberdashers' Company,
Sue Hammerson's Charitable Trust, Help a London Child,
Imperial Chemical Industries plc, The Inverforth Charitable Trust,
John Lewis Partnership plc, The Ian Karten Trust,
Mathilda and Terence Kennedy Charitable Trust, Konditor & Cook,
The Lambert Charitable Trust, Corporation of London,
The Lynn Foundation, Manches & Co, Marks and Spencer plc,
The Milbourn Charitable Trust, The Peter Minet Trust,
Peter Moores Foundation, Newcomen Collett Foundation,
PricewaterhouseCoopers, Railtrack plc, The Rayne Foundation,
The Reuter Foundation, Royal and Sun Alliance Insurance Group plc,
Sir Walter St John's Educational Charity, St Olave's and St Saviour's
Grammar School Foundation, Simon's Charity, Singer & Friedlander Ltd
Snipe Charitable Trust, South West Trains Limited,
The Stanley Foundation Ltd, Sir John Swire CBE and Lady Swire,
The Vandervell Foundation, Garfield Weston Foundation,
The Whitbread 1988 Charitable Trust,
The Harold Hyam Wingate Foundation

and our many Friends of the Young Vic

The Young Vic gratefully acknowledges
a French Theatre Season Award for research into French Theatre

The Young Vic on the World Wide Web is supported by Direct Connection

The Young Vic is supported by: London Arts Board,
the London Borough of Lambeth, London Borough Grants,
the London Borough of Southwark, and the National Lottery,
issued through the Arts Council of England.

PRODUCTION ACKNOWLEDGEMENTS

Puppets made by
Vicki Hallam, Sofie Layton, Sean Myatt,
Peter O'Rourke and Lucy Turner

Student placement from Boston University: David Lurie

Subsidised rehearsal facilities provided by the Jerwood Space

We gratefully acknowledge the assistance of **Persil** *Comfort* **Persil** *finesse* courtesy of Lever Brothers Ltd., in providing Wardrobe Care.

With thanks to
Shakespeare's Globe Theatre
Eastway Offset Printers
Sparks Theatrical Hire

THE YOUNG VIC COMPANY

For the safety and comfort of patrons, smoking is not permitted
in the auditorium. In accordance with the requirements of the
London Borough of Lambeth persons shall not be permitted to stand
or sit in any of the gangways. If standing be permitted in the gangways
and at the rear of the seating, it shall be limited to the numbers
indicated on notices exhibited in those positions.

PHOTOGRAPHY OR RECORDING IS NOT PERMITTED
IN THE AUDITORIUM.

PLEASE ENSURE THAT ALL MOBILE TELEPHONES, PAGERS AND WATCH ALARMS ARE SWITCHED OFF BEFORE ENTERING THE AUDITORIUM

COMING SOON AT THE YOUNG VIC

Main House

3 February–11 March 2000

*The Young Vic Theatre Company and
the Royal Shakespeare Company present*

A Servant to Two Masters

By Carlo Goldoni

in a new translation by Lee Hall
directed by Tim Supple

22 June–22 July 2000

The Royal Shakespeare Company presents

Tales From Ovid

by Ted Hughes

directed by Tim Supple

Studio

17 November–11 December 1999

Wink Productions presents

Strike Gently, Away From Body

14 December–24 December 1999

Theatre-Rites presents

The Lost and Moated Land

A magical journey for under-fives

11 January–29 January 2000

Kaboodle Musical Theatre presents

Soho Story

The Nativity
David Farr

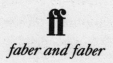

faber and faber

First published in 1999
by Faber and Faber Limited
3 Queen Square London WC1N 3AU

Typeset by Country Setting, Kingsdown, Kent CT14 8ES
Printed in England by Mackays of Chatham plc, Chatham, Kent

A CIP record for this book
is available from the British Library

ISBN 0-571-20466-X

2 4 6 8 10 9 7 5 3 1

Characters

Joseph
Villagers
Village Children
Mary
Mary's Father
Aaron
Wedding Guests
Bridesmaids
Mary and Joseph's Donkey
Beggar/Gabriel
Herod
Herod's Serving Girl
Minister of Justice
Water Seller
Abraham
Sarah
Isaac
Isaac's Midwives
Two Trusty Men
God
Talking Bush
Goliath
David
Warriors
Solomon
Officer
Two Prostitutes
Market Traders
The Devil (Old Man)
The Devil's Men

Ezra the Innkeeper
Herod's Attendants
Three Shepherds
Benjamin
Benjamin's Mad Sheep
Spies
Caspar
Melchior
Balthazar
Herod's Commander
Soldiers
Innocents
Choir of Angels

Various sheep, horses, donkeys, camels
and other animals

This text went to press before the opening night
and may therefore differ from the version
as performed

Act One

ONE: THE ANNUNCIATION

*A man. A poor man. Forty years old. Quiet, dignified,
but resigned.*
  Joseph the carpenter.

A Voice in the Dark Joseph loved wood.

*Wood falls from the sky, scattering around Joseph.
He starts to work.*
  A circle of villagers gathers to watch him.

Villagers Joseph lived in a small village in one of the
most remote Northern districts of Galilee. The land was
poor, the sun baked down, rain almost never fell. The
men worked the barren fields to produce what food they
could for their families. The women slaved at home,
making the most of the meagre crop. The children wore
simple clothes and built their toys from whatever they
could find. But once a year they would receive a special
toy from Joseph the carpenter.

The tools of the shop make music as he works.
  A group of children.

Child 1 Joseph? Will you make me a toy?

Child 2 Joseph, will you make me one too?

Child 3 Joseph. Will you make me a toy?

Child 4 And me!

Child 5 And me!

Child 6 And me!

Joseph He built toys for all the children in the district!

Villager But other people's children. Joseph the carpenter had no children of his own.

A family rush in. Joseph presents them with a beautiful wooden kite.

Mother Thank you, Joseph. It's beautiful.

Girl Why aren't you married, Joseph?

Mother Sshhh, Leah. That is none of your business.

They leave, the girl flying the kite, which soars into the air. Joseph watches sadly as she plays with the kite.

Joseph Joseph was forty years old and still he had no wife. His brothers had wives, his friends had wives and children. Beautiful children. But Joseph did not.
Because when it came to women, Joseph was unbelievably . . . shy!

Joseph and a girl, eighteen. The girl likes Joseph.

Girl Hello, Joseph. How are you?

Joseph . . .

The girl waits a while as Joseph struggles to speak, then she yawns and runs away with another young man. Joseph hits himself in despair.

Joseph had resigned himself to never falling in love!

Villager And then, one day . . .

A storm breaks over the village. The scene dissolves. The rain pours. Clouds fly across the sky. Great wind and rain pour from the heavens.

Village Boy A storm broke over the village. The wind poured dark clouds across the sky and rain fell in torrents! No one had ever seen a storm like it!

An Old Man (*to his grandson*) It is a message of anger from God! Hurry inside and close the shutters!

The shutters of all the village bang shut against the wind and rain. Clack. Clack. Clack.
A beautiful girl. Caught in the rain. Running home. She is fifteen. Feisty and free-spirited. She is Mary. She is soaked to the bone.

Mary A young girl was caught playing in the pouring rain. She loved it! But then she got cold. She was far from her cottage and could find no shelter. (*She seeks the nearest shelter but everywhere is barred up.*) Let me in! Let me in!
Finally she found an open door. Inside was a shop filled with wonderful things. She remembered it from her childhood. But it was the first time she had been inside for years!

Joseph It was Joseph's shop.

It is Joseph's shop. He is alone amidst the fruits of his life's work. Mary enters.
Joseph is carving a piece of wood. He looks at her fearfully.

Mary May I wait inside until the storm is over?

Joseph . . .

Joseph nods awkwardly. He returns to his work. Mary stands politely.

Joseph had never seen such a beautiful girl in all his life. He was terrified!

Mary You must be Joseph.

Joseph . . .

Mary I am Mary.

3

Joseph . . .

Mary laughs and dances round the room.

Mary What are you making?

Joseph Oh. It's a . . . a . . .
All of a sudden, Joseph had forgotten the word for what he was making!
It's a . . . a . . .

Mary A chair?

He shakes his head.

A bed?

No, not a bed. Joseph mimes it.

Maybe a shelf? A bookcase?

Joseph No! it's a . . .

Mary A bench! A stool! A table!

Joseph Yes! A table. A table!

Mary Mary liked the man. He was different to the boys who were always chasing her and trying to impress her. (*She comes closer.*) How many tables have you made?

Joseph A lot.

Mary As many as there are stars in the sky?

Joseph More.

Mary As many as there are grains of sand in the desert?

Joseph More!

Mary Show me your hands.

Joseph shows her his hands. She touches them.

When Mary touched the carpenter's hands, a strange feeling awoke in her.

Joseph When Joseph felt the girl's young hands on his, he knew he had fallen in love.

The pots in Joseph's kitchen sing.
Still Mary holds Joseph's hands. She finds them quite beautiful.

Mary They looked at each other as the storm raged!

Joseph The look seemed to last an eternity!

Mary Mary waited for him to say something! Anything!

Joseph But Joseph was struck dumb.

The storm passes.

Mary The storm has passed.

Joseph Yes.

Mary I must go.

Joseph . . .
And she left!
No, come back! I love you completely and utterly and I want to marry you.
Too late. She's gone!
For three whole days, Joseph did nothing but think of the girl. For the first time in his life he couldn't work properly! He made tables with legs of different heights, chairs with only three legs! He talked to the hammer as if it were her. He held nails like they were her fingers!
I love you. I love you. Marry me!

Mary Mary rushed to her room and tried to forget this fateful meeting. But all she could dream of was him. Days passed! Interminable days!
Why doesn't he come?

Joseph Joseph was in turmoil!
I could go to her father and ask for her hand. But she will certainly reject me!

Mary Mary was sick with love! She locked the door of her room and determined to starve until he came!

Joseph I will not go!

Mary He must come!

Joseph But all I can think of is her! What should I do? Finally he could bear it no more!

The father arrives.

He rushed to the house of her father and knocked! I am here to ask for the hand of . . . of . . .

An agonising silence as Joseph fails to say the name of his beloved. Then, thankfully . . .

Mary's Father Say it, Joseph, and she is yours. She has been waiting for you.

Flowers fall. Joseph hugs Mary.

Villagers Three months later they were married! The whole village brought flowers and fruit to celebrate this strange union! No one could believe it. Joseph the carpenter, who couldn't speak to a girl without falling over, married, and to the most beautiful girl in the village!

A wedding banquet.

Mary's Father Mary's father gave a long and heartfelt speech . . . (*He gives a long speech during which people fall asleep.*)

Aaron And Joseph's brother spoke of Joseph as a good and kind man that would make Mary very happy.

Applause.

Guest There was drinking and dancing!

Music and a dance.

6

Another Guest And magic tricks!

Magic tricks.

Another Guest And jokes!

Jokes.

Another Guest And everyone got wonderfully merry!

Drunken walking.

Joseph Except Mary. She seemed distracted. (*to her*) What is wrong my love? This is the happiest day of my life. But your face is clouded by a worry. Do you wish you had not married me?

Mary It's not that. I will tell you when we are alone.

The party disappears.

Joseph We are alone. Now tell me.

Mary I cannot come to your bed tonight as a wife should.

Joseph If you need time, take it. I have waited long enough, I can wait another day.

Mary I may not come then either.

Joseph Then when? How long must I wait? I want to have a child with you.

Mary staggers and falls.

What is it?

Mary I feel sick. Dizzy. (*She weeps.*)

Joseph Tell me. Whatever it is I will love you forever.

Mary turns. She smiles a radiant smile.

Mary You will?

Joseph Yes my love!

Mary Then know. I am pregnant.

A shutter slams in the night.

Joseph Joseph was chilled to the core of his being. His wife, pregnant with another man's child on the day of his wedding!
Whose is it? What trick have you played on me?

Mary It is no man's.

Joseph You want me to raise another man's child! You know what the law says. A woman who is caught being unfaithful will be stoned!

Mary It is no man's!

Joseph I will annul the marriage and hide you in the mountains where your shame will be kept secret from the village. Although you have betrayed and misused me I do not wish you to come to any harm. I love you too much.

Mary Joseph! Do you believe?

Joseph Yes of course.

Mary Then listen and believe!
I was in my room preparing for the wedding day . . .

Bridesmaids (*rushing in*) With your bridesmaids!

Mary When a beggar man came knocking.

Beggar Charity!

Bridesmaids Away, dirty rat! This is a wedding day!

Beggar Charity!

Bridesmaid Away, scoundrel, before I pour water on your head!

Beggar Charity!

The bridesmaids proceed to pour water over his head. But the water misses him and they soak each other instead.

Bridesmaids Aaah! You've ruined our dresses! Get out! Get out!

Mary No, wait. Come in. (*to the bridesmaids*) Fetch me my bag.

The bridesmaids run out.

We were left alone. His clothes were old and he smelt of rotten grass and foul water. But his eyes kept staring at me. Then he spoke.

Beggar I am the Angel Gabriel.

Mary (*giggling*) You're who?

Beggar I am the Angel Gabriel.

Mary Hello. I'm the Queen of Sheba!

The beggar transforms into an angel. The windows clatter and sing.

Mary Oh my.

Gabriel You have a child in your belly. It is the child of God. In nine months you will give birth. Until that time, your husband may not sleep with you. For yours will be a virgin birth. And your child will be the new-born king, born to rule over Israel.
This is your fate. Believe.

Mary I believe.

Bridesmaids The bridesmaids returned!

Mary I rushed to show them the angel!
But only the beggar remained.

Beggar Charity!

Joseph The story is impossible! Madness. But your eyes speak truth. My reason says your story must be false. My heart says it is true. Which is right? (*He walks out under the moon.*) Joseph ran out of the room and walked under the moon and cried out.

My reason tells me one thing but my heart another! Which is right? Is it true what she says?

The Leaves of the Trees The wind rose and spoke to him through the leaves of the lemon trees.
True. True.

Joseph What? What did you say?

The Leaves of the Trees True. True.

The Birds in the Trees True! True!

Joseph But I need proof!

The beggar passes through the trees.

Beggar He who needs proof is damned.

Joseph Who are you?

But the beggar disappears.

And nature spoke to him in all its glory!

Nature in All its Glory Believe!

Joseph runs into his house and kneels before Mary.

Joseph Forgive me. I believe you. And I love you!

Mary I love you!

And Mary's belly grows like magic as . . .

. . . Herod is carried in on a richly clothed couch in his palace of gold, his feet being massaged by serving girls.

Herod's Serving Girls Eight months later!

Herod In his luxurious and spacious palace in the heart of Jerusalem, King Herod was anxiously awaiting some important news.

Distant screaming rises and fades. Herod listens intently.

Minister of Justice (*entering*) My lord.

Herod What news, Minister of Justice?

Minister of Justice The men who tried to assassinate you this morning have been caught, fairly tried, tortured and executed.

Herod Very good. Did they confess?

Minister of Justice No my lord. They maintained a total silence, only opening their mouths to curse you as a corrupt and despotic tyrant.

Herod Liars! Traitors!

Minister of Justice At least now you may sleep easy in your bed.

Herod (*relaxing*) Ah yes. Sweet sleep! (*then worried again*) But what if others try the same thing? You are my Minister of Justice. This must never happen again!

Minister of Justice My lord, it would be easier to police the people if we knew who they were and where they lived.

Herod But there are so many of the little rats. How would we do that?

Minister of Justice Command everyone in the country to register for a census.

Herod Brilliant! I will do so immediately.

Herod turns and speaks to his people (the audience).

I am issuing the following decree. A census of the population will take place one month from today. Every man and woman in the land must travel to . . . to . . . (*He sticks his finger on the royal map at random and plucks a name.*) Bethlehem! And register. No one is exempt! Young and old. The healthy and the lame. The blind and the insane. All must proceed to Bethlehem. This is the word of the king!

In the village, Mary is heavily pregnant. She heaves a saddle-pack towards the waiting donkey.

Joseph Joseph and Mary borrowed a donkey from Mary's father.

Mary The road to Bethlehem was over a hundred miles. Mary's back hurt from the weight of the baby and she dreaded the journey.
Do we have to go now?

Joseph It is the word of the king.

They set off, Joseph leading. The sun rises.

The Samarian desert stretched out before them. The sun beat down above them. All around them: emptiness.

Mary On the first day they were jaunty and full of enthusiasm.

Joseph On the second day they were determined and full of confidence.

Mary On the third day they were resilient and full of fine words.

Joseph On the fourth day they were tired but happy.

Mary On the fifth day they ran out of food.

Joseph On the sixth day they ran out of water.

Mary On the seventh day they collapsed . . .

They fall to the ground, exhausted.
A poor waterseller woman appears.

Waterseller . . . by the side of the road.
Where are you heading, strangers?

Joseph To Bethlehem.

Mary To register for the census.

Joseph Word of the king.

Mary Who are you?

Waterseller I am a waterseller.

Mary A waterseller! Oh please, please, give us water . . .

Joseph We need water . . .

Mary We have been travelling for seven days and our supply has run out.

Waterseller I have none.

Joseph What?

Waterseller There has been no rain for eight months. The well is dry.

Mary No water? But I have to have water for the child!

They look around them in despair.

Are we to die here?

Joseph Why would God be so cruel?

Mary Maybe we have done something to anger him.

Joseph Maybe we are not good enough.

Mary Maybe he has abandoned us.

Joseph Maybe he has left us to die.

Pause.

Waterseller Dear friends, you seem disheartened. Let me tell you a story that will restore your faith.

Abraham appears. An old man. Small, terribly thin, but upright. Inscrutable.

Long ago in this land there lived a good man. He was called Abraham.

Sarah, his wife, appears.

And he had a wife called Sarah. She was old and beyond child-bearing age. But God visited her and gave her a child.

The Village A miracle!

Sarah gives birth to Isaac.

Midwives A boy! They called him Isaac. He grew into a healthy lad.

The waterseller becomes Isaac.

Sheep One day, Abraham was tending his sheep when God spoke to him.

God Here I am.

Abraham My God, what do you want of me?

God You have a son Isaac. Take him to the holy mountain and burn him as a sacrifice.

Sheep Abraham did not ask why, but said:

Abraham I will do as you ask, my Lord.

Sheep Sarah burst into tears and tried to hold on to Isaac.

Sarah Do not take him! He is our only son!

Abraham Trust God.

Isaac Where are we going, father?

Abraham We are going to sacrifice a lamb on the holy mountain.

Trusty Man 1 He took two trusty men and travelled to the mountain. Then Abraham said to his men.

Abraham Wait here for me. I will return.

Trusty Man 2 Father and son climbed. Abraham carried the wood for the fire.

They climb the mountain.

As they were climbing, Isaac the boy asked:

Isaac Father. I see the wood to burn. And the tinder to create fire. But where is the lamb we are sacrificing? I don't see it.

Trusty Man 1 And Abraham replied . . .

Abraham God will provide the lamb.

Trusty Man 2 And Abraham remained noble, but Isaac became afraid.

Isaac I still do not see the lamb we are to sacrifice, father.

Abraham God will provide the lamb.

Trusty Man 1 They reached the top of the mountain.

Isaac I still do not see the lamb.

Trusty Man 1 Abraham looked to the sky.

Trusty Man 2 Silence.

Abraham sighs a deep sigh of sorrow.

Abraham I must tie you down.

Isaac No!

He ties his screaming son to the wood and lays him on the altar.

Trusty Man 1 Then Abraham took a knife from his belt.

Trusty Man 2 And held it aloft above the head of his son.

Isaac No!

Trusty Man 1 No!

Joseph No!

Trusty Man 2 No!

Mary No!

Abraham puts the knife to his son's neck.
A mad screaming.
Sudden clap of thunder. Darkness. Then light. Isaac is free. A ram has replaced him.
Abraham holds his son, shaking with emotion.

Abraham Thank you, my God.

Waterseller Faith is like water. Without it we wither and die. Because Abraham had faith he was rewarded. And his son Isaac grew old and wise and gave birth to Jacob, after whom this well is named.

Another clap of thunder. The waterseller dances. Rain falls on Joseph and Mary. They drink together and are jubilant. They dance in the rain.

Mary The heavens opened and a great rain fell!
They drunk at Jacob's Well!

They continue, Joseph leading purposefully.

Joseph In two weeks they crossed the Samarian desert.

Mary And reached the great stone mountains of the interior.
Joseph?

Joseph Yes, my love.

Mary Can we go round the mountains?

Joseph No, we have to go over them.

Mary (*looking at the most enormous of the mountains*)
And that highest one whose peak seems to pierce the sky.
Do we have to climb that one?

Joseph There is no other way across.

Mary (*suddenly terrified, drawing back*) I cannot climb
that mountain.

Joseph (*starting to climb*) Of course you can. It's like
that old woman said. Have faith. Of course it will be
hard, tiring. But together . . .

*Joseph continues offering silent encouragement as
Mary says:*

Mary But as Joseph spoke, and as they climbed, Mary
felt the world turn around her like a spinning top, faster
and faster . . .

*The world spins. Mary falls down, grabbing the
ground.*

Joseph Mary! What is it?

Mary looks up at him, breathless.

Mary I am afraid.

Joseph What of?

Mary I'm too high. I'm going to fall off . . . You can go on without me.

Joseph But you'll die of cold!

Mary Then I'll go home.

Joseph (*coming down*) Mary, come back!

Mary (*to God*) You should never have chosen me! I am not good enough!

The Bush Do not turn back.

Mary Mary had stopped next to an old bush. It was barren, as dead as the mountain itself.

The Bush Or you will never reach your destination.

Mary Who is talking?

The Bush I am a Samaritan. I was cast out by my family and left to die in the mountains. For many years I have lived in this bush. But this is no place for a pregnant woman. You must go on.

Mary I will never get over this mountain.

The Bush (*comfortingly*) Never lose hope. Remember the story that tells us there is always hope.

> *David appears, aged eight.*

Long ago in the town to which you are heading was born a boy called David. Even as a child David was a fighter.

David (*aged eight*) I'll fight anyone! (*He challenges the audience to a fight.*) Come on! Come on then! Fight me! Who's going to fight me? I'm the best fighter in my class. And I can play the harp. But I like fighting best!

The Bush During David's youth, Israel was at war.

The shouts and sounds of war.

A Warrior The enemy was the Philistines. And the Philistines had one fighter, greater and more fearsome than any other. Goliath!

Goliath appears. He is colossal, towering over Joseph and Mary.
Goliath roars and the Israelites scatter in terror. His shadow falls over Mary and Joseph. Goliath laughs and booms his challenge.

Goliath Who will fight me? If any Israelite fights and kills me, then let all Philistines be the servants of Israel! But if I kill them, you Israelites will be our slaves forever!

The Bush No Israelite warrior would dare accept the giant's challenge.

Goliath Will no one fight me?

Various Israelite Warriors Uh, no thanks. Not today. Got an injury.

Goliath (*disappointed*) I want a fight!

Warriors Sorry.

The Bush No one would fight the giant. The Israelites seemed destined to fall under the power of the Philistines forever. When . . .

David's Voice (*aged thirteen*) I'll fight you!

Goliath What? Did I hear a mouse squeak?

The Bush Goliath tried to see whose voice had spoken. He peered down amongst the Israelites, who desperately struggled to hide the thirteen-year-old David.

Frightened Israelite Warrior I didn't hear anything. Did you hear anything?

Goliath I heard a voice!

Frightened Israelite Warrior No, honest, it must have been a mouse.

Second Israelite Warrior Or a bat.

David (*from under the cloak of an Israelite*) I'll fight anyone!

Goliath There!

Frightened Israelite Warrior A mouse again.

Second Israelite Warrior They're everywhere. It's the heat.

Goliath Who is he who dares to challenge Goliath?

David sneaks from under the skirts of the warriors.

David It is I! David!

He sees Goliath. Goliath sees him.

Ooh.

Goliath Ha ha ha ha. Ha ha ha HA HA HA!

David (*angry at being laughed at*) All right. I'll fight you! You big bully!

Goliath (*wiping tears from his eyes*) Ha ha ha. Oh dear. Oh dear.

David Come on then!

Goliath I'll snap you in two and stir my coffee with your legs and scatter your hair on my soup like pepper!

David Just you try!

David runs between Goliath's legs.

The Bush David ran to the river by his home, and found five smooth stones.

David One, two, three, four, five . . .

The Bush He made a sling from a branch of an old tree and a piece of cloth, and returned to the battleground.

David (*returning*) Let battle commence!

Goliath You're for the crows, boy!

> *Goliath advances flailing his sword in the air. David ducks and leaps to avoid the swishing blade.*

Ha ha ha ha ha! Where are you, fly? I'll kill you for my sport!

> *But David produces one of his stones and aims the sling at the giant. The stone flies true and straight. It smashes into the forehead of the giant. Goliath stops, shocked.*

Oh.

> *Goliath explodes and crashes to the earth in pieces. David is picked up by the warriors and the trumpets blazon loud.*

Warriors David for King!

The Bush And the Philistines were defeated and David became King. That is why they say that hope springs eternal. Because with hope, we are never beaten.

Mary (*looking at the mountain*) I can climb that mountain. (*Lifted by hope, Mary climbs the mountain.*)

Joseph On the twentieth day they approached Jerusalem.
Let's stay in Jerusalem for one night before heading for Bethlehem. You will be comfortable and we will be fresh for our final journey.

Mary But the night before, as she slept by the side of the road, Mary had a dream.

A crow flies high in the air, swooping over the sleeping Mary before diving down to rip open her belly. Mary fights the crow off, screaming.
Joseph, sleeping beside Mary, is woken.

Joseph Mary! Wake up! Wake up! You are dreaming!

Mary We must not go through Jerusalem. There is evil there.

Joseph But you need shelter, food.

Mary There is evil there! I saw it in my dream!

Joseph You shouldn't believe your dreams!

Mary A crow swooped and devoured my belly.

Joseph How many more dreams will you have? How many more angels and devils must you see before we can reach Bethlehem?

Mary Mary fell silent. Never had Joseph spoken to her like this. (*to him*) I did not ask for this child. But now it has happened I celebrate it. I love it. But you may not. Look at me. If you do not love me, then leave. Go to Jerusalem. I will continue alone.

Joseph debates what to do.

Donkey The donkey intervened.
May I make a point about love at this juncture?

Joseph What did you say?

Donkey Don't look so surprised. Donkeys have opinions too, you know.

Joseph Oh, great.

Donkey Your sad quarrel reminds me of a story my grandfather told me. He had it told him by his grandfather, who had had it related to him by his mother, who in turn . . .

Mary We get the point.

Donkey Well, it all goes back to a distant donkey ancestor of mine, who was an ass in the court of King Solomon!

The donkey leads us into a luscious ancient court. The young King Solomon sits thinking. An officer runs in.

Officer There is a dispute, my king. Between two women of the night.

Solomon Admit them.

The officer returns carrying a baby. Two colourfully dressed prostitutes follow, arguing viciously.

Woman 1 The baby is mine.

Woman 2 He is mine! My lord . . .

Woman 1 My king!

Woman 2 My master!

Woman 1 My liege!

Woman 2 I have been wronged!

Woman 1 I have been abused!

Woman 2 Shamefully wronged!

Woman 1 Disgracefully abused!

Solomon raises his staff. Silence.

Solomon You. Tell your story.

Woman 1 My lord, I am a working woman. I become pregnant. One week ago, I give birth to this beautiful boy. I look in his eyes and see my own. I hold his little head in my hands, and I cry tears of joy. I vow to look after him with all my heart.

Three days later, she also gave birth to a son. But she did not look after him. She put too many covers on him at night and the poor little thing suffocated. So she came in the night while I was sleeping and replaced mine with hers! Now she says mine is the dead baby and this beauty you hold in your hands is hers! (*She breaks down and weeps.*)

Solomon And what do you say to this?

Woman 2 It is true what she says, all of it. Except for one thing. It is I whose baby is alive, and hers who is dead! And it is she who stole my baby that you hold before you!

Woman 1 It is my baby that you hold!

Woman 2 It is my baby!

Donkey As my ancestor tells the story, King Solomon stood and traced a large circle with his staff. No one spoke a word!

Solomon You. Stand on that side. And you on the other.

The women do as ordered. Solomon places the baby in the middle of the circle.

Both of you, take the baby by its arm.

The women approach.

Pull.

Woman 2 What?

Solomon Whoever wants the baby most will win it.

Woman 1 Let us start!

Solomon Begin!

Woman 2 No!

Solomon Pull!

Joseph No!

Woman 2 No, let her keep it. It is her child. I was lying. Please. She can take it! Just do not kill it!

The first woman wrenches the baby out of her grasp and holds it aloft like a trophy.

Woman 1 He is mine!

Solomon Now we know who is the mother.

Officer Who?

Donkey Who?

Joseph (*rushing into the scene*) Who? Who?

A pause. Solomon approaches Joseph and hands him the baby.

Solomon You decide. Who loves the child more?

A pause as Joseph thinks. Then he takes the baby and gives it to the second woman.

Joseph Take your son. For you would rather lose your child and see it live, than try to keep it and thus see it die. That is true love.

Solomon Now be gone!

And they are. The donkey remains.

Donkey My ancestor tells it like this. Faith sustains us. Hope inspires us. But without love we are nothing. Love is our blood.

Joseph and Mary look at each other.

Joseph We will not go through Jerusalem.

Donkey Good. Onward to Bethlehem! And no more talk of stupid asses!

THREE: THE BIRTH

A gaggle of market traders and low lifes parade the stage, boasting their wares and their wiles. Card sharps, whores, gamesters, con men, quacks, traders and charlatans. Welcome to the market.

Card Sharp Bethlehem was packed with thousands of people arriving to pay the tax.

Trader People with time on their hands and money in their pockets!

Con Man Original star of David! The very one he wore when he killed the giant! One for fifty, two for a pound.

Trader Get your signed picture of Herod here!

Card Sharp Follow the queen and double your money!

Whore Follow this queen and you won't care about money!

Quack Diseases, plagues and afflictions cured in an instant! Witness the blind seeing and the lame walking.

An obviously planted blind man rises.

Blind Man I can see. Oh, you worker of miracles, you healer of the damned!

Quack This could be you, ladies and gentlemen!

Spice Seller Take this spice every morning and live forever!

Crystal Ball Seller Learn your fortune! See into the mists of the future and all will become clear!

Palmist Have your hand read! If you don't like what you hear, have the other read for half price!

Joseph Joseph and Mary entered the city at dusk.

People bustle past Joseph and Mary.

Mary Mary was knocked from side to side by the throngs of people buying and selling, drinking, fighting, yelling and screaming.

Joseph They fought their way through the teeming crowds until they reached the centre.
We must find somewhere to stay.

The traders and hawkers rush over to ensnare them.

Traders Stars of David! Small Noah's arks! Buy two replica ten commandments tablets and I'll throw in a Moses basket for free!

Joseph Let us through!

Quack Make way! I'm a doctor. This woman needs my help!

Palmist Let me read your palm for the child! You must be a very proud father! This way for a reading!

Joseph and Mary are physically separated by the traders.

Mary Joseph!

Joseph Mary! Where are you?

Spice Seller Take this spice for eternal life!

Trader Get your signed picture of Herod here!

Card Sharp Follow the queen and double your money!

Joseph Let me go!

Crystal Ball Seller I can see the baby in my ball. It's a girl! A beautiful bright-faced girl. A silver coin and I'll tell you more!

Mary Joseph!

Joseph Let go of me! Mary!

They are lifted in the air and valiantly fight their way back together. Mary hugs Joseph tight.

Mary I lost you.

Joseph Here I am.

The traders circle the couple, menacingly whispering their offers and sales.

We're not buying anything. We just want somewhere to stay for the night!

Sellers You won't find a room now. Not at this time. The place is packed. Look around you! Ha ha ha. Ha ha ha.

They look around. 'No Vacancy' signs meet them wherever they go.

Mary We must find a room!

An Old Man I have a room.

Joseph An old man stood before them. His head was shaped like an egg. His face was pale, as if he had not seen the sun in centuries.

Mary Where is it?

Old Man Not far from here. In the middle of town.

Joseph What kind of room?

Old Man The best. A large bed of red velvet. Covers of the purest silk. Pillows of feathers from African swans. Carpets woven from the wool of the Eastern lands. Curtains of fine lace spun by ancient hands.

Joseph (*awestruck*) How much is it?

Old Man Normally I charge two gold coins per night.

Joseph Two gold coins!

Old Man And it should by rights be more. It's very busy at the moment, everyone is here for the tax. It's the loveliest room in my house, and my house is the finest house in the whole town.

Joseph and Mary We have nothing like this money!

Old Man But seeing as the lady is expecting . . . you shall have it for nothing.

Mary and Joseph Oh, thank you. Thank you. Please take us there!

Joseph They tried to kiss the old man's hand.

Mary But he drew back in disgust.

Old Man We have no time for this frivolity! Come with me!

   They start to walk.

Joseph They followed the old man. But soon they saw they were starting to leave the centre.
   I thought you said your house was in the centre of the town.

Old Man My house is in the new centre. It is superior to the old centre.

Mary Suddenly the baby kicked in Mary's stomach. It was like a warning.
   Who is this man?

   Now shadowy figures join the old man. Now another. Now two more. And another two.

Joseph Who are these men?

Old Man My sons.

Mary Why do they all limp?

Old Man It is a flaw in the family.

Joseph Further and further they walked into the darkest part of the town. No lights came from the windows of the houses. Silence surrounded them.

The men light flame torches as the darkness descends.

Please. It is getting dark. Take us back. Take us back to the centre.

Old Man No rooms in the centre.

Mary You said you lived in the centre. You liar!

The men turn. Dark shadows in the street.

Man You come with us.

Another Man There is no way back.

Another Man And we are almost there.

The Men Look.

Joseph They looked and saw a small dark house in the darkest corner of the street.

Mary It was black as coal, as if it had suffered a great fire and yet not fallen. The windows were boarded up. The doorway hung open.

Joseph I thought you said yours was the finest house in the town.

Old Man Wait until you see inside . . . Come.

They enter the house.

Joseph They entered and were greeted by a spiral staircase leading down for as far as they could see. The air smelt of smoke and burning flesh.

Old Man Come.

Joseph Where are the carpets from the Eastern lands?

Old Man It is all waiting for you. Come.

Mary The baby kicked again. What does it mean?

Joseph Down they went, further and further, until they reached a small windowless room. It was hotter than the desert sun.

Mary Inside there was nothing.

Joseph No bed.

Mary No curtains.

Joseph No window.

Mary No light. Nothing.
  You said this was the loveliest room in your house!

Joseph You promised us pillows of swan's feathers, and curtains of the finest silk!

Old Man And you shall have them. You shall have it all my friends, everything that you desire!
  But first you must give me what I want.

Joseph I'm not giving you two gold coins for this room!

Old Man I don't want two gold coins.

Joseph Then what do you want?

  The old man stops dead and points to Mary's belly.

Old Man I want him.

Mary And Mary heard a small voice inside her, as if it was the voice of the child itself, saying this man is the devil, and this place is called hell.

  Mary and Joseph look at each other.

Old Man Give me the child and I will make you richer and more powerful than Herod himself.

Refuse, and I will tear the child from your belly and leave you here to rot for eternity.

They look around. The men stare intently at Mary's belly. A drumming begins.

Mary I will never give birth here.

Old Man I'll give you everything! The earth will be your garden! Just give me the child!

Mary Never!

Old Man Give me the child or die!

Joseph Never!

Old Man Then I must take him from you.

The men don cloaks and masks, macabre versions of operating theatre costume.
Mary and Joseph stand in horror. The men circle the pregnant woman.

Joseph Mary, run!

Mary No, wait! Have faith, Joseph.

The men bring out operating instruments. They stamp the ground with their feet and circle closer. Then suddenly they take hold of Mary. An operating table appears and they lay her on it.

Mary Have faith, Joseph!

The men hold their knives and scalpels above Mary and chant.

Believe!

Joseph I believe!

The men make to bring down their knives upon Mary's belly.

A great screaming is heard. It is from the devils themselves, as they see to their horror that Mary has disappeared.

Old Man (*in a rage of horror*) Where is she? Where is she? Find her! Kill her!

Joseph But when they started to look for Mary, they all saw her face in each other's.

The Men She is here! No, she is here! No, she is here!

Joseph And in their rage they started to attack themselves!

They attack each other, chopping limbs and heads off, until nothing exists of any of them but their black, smoking cloaks.

The Men Aaaaaaaah!

The screams of the men in an eternity of torture fade into the dark night . . .

Joseph (*standing alone*) Mary? Mary, where are you? Mary!!

Mary Hello, Joseph.

Mary appears unharmed.

Joseph But I saw them, with the knives . . . They were . . . Where are they? Where are we?
They were back on the street. The night was quiet and still. And of the devil's hotel, there was no sign. It was as if it had never existed.

Mary Suddenly they heard singing.

A fat innkeeper enters drunkenly. He sings.

Innkeeper
  My inn is full
  My belly is full
  My pockets are full
  Ah, life is wonderful!

  He belches a huge belch.

My inn hasn't been as full as this since the weekend after
the earth tremor. And that day I forgot to charge anyone!
Well, not this time! Who said I was too soft to make
money! Ha! I've made a fortune! Soft Ezra indeed.
Crafty schemer Ezra more like. Money-grabbing-old-fox
Ezra the innkeeper. Cunning-as-a-panther Ezra. Grrrr.
Grrr.
  Ah, the night sky looks so beautiful when you've just
made a fortune! Each star like a small coin. And the
moon a big silver one! Ha ha ha. Everything's beautiful.
Even my wife looks beautiful tonight. I might even sleep
in the same bed as her. I might. (*He belches again.*) I'm
charging double the normal rate. Per person. One room's
got twenty people in! If I wasn't so happy I'd have to
feel a bit guilty. Guilty? Panther-fox Ezra feeling guilt?
Don't know the meaning of the word.
  Oh yes, tonight's a night to get drunk and celebrate
one's winnings. Tonight, Ezra the innkeeper, drunken
Ezra, fat sow Ezra, is a winner! A winner!
  Come on, let's count the money again. I know how
much there is but it's such fun! (*He takes out his bag of
coins and lays them on the floor.*) One, two, three, four,
five . . .

Mary Excuse me?

Innkeeper Sorry, we're completely full and anyway
I doubt you could afford my exorbitant rates. Six, seven,
eight . . .

Mary Excuse me.

Innkeeper Now look what you've done. I have to start again now.

Mary What are you doing?

Innkeeper I'm counting the money that I have so ruthlessly procured from ordinary people.

Joseph So we heard.

Innkeeper Yes, there's no denying it. I'm a bad man. A rough sort. You can trust me as far as you can throw me. Which isn't far. You know the type. No human feelings at all. Not a sensitive bone in my body. Money money money. That's my sole concern. (*He looks closer.*) Oh my God, you're pregnant. Oh, you poor girl. What are you doing out on a night like this?

Mary We've been trying to find a place to stay.

Innkeeper Oh that's terrible. And you look so tired. When's it due?

Mary Any time now.

Innkeeper Oh that's wonderful. My wife and I, we have two boys and a girl. They're so lovely. The day my daughter was born was the happiest day of my life. Her little fat face . . . (*He weeps.*) She was so beautiful and chubby . . . the midwife said she'd never seen bigger. You'll make good parents, I can see you will. Can I touch it?

Mary If you like.

Innkeeper touches it.

Innkeeper Oh yes, beautiful, beautiful baby. Very round. It's a good sign. Now, where was I?

Joseph You were counting your money.

Innkeeper Oh, that can wait. Childbirth – it's a miracle, it really is. So you poor people, you have nowhere to stay . . . Let me think . . . let me think . . . I must be able to help . . .

The innkeeper does some exaggerated thinking and walking around.
What he doesn't notice is that a thief has seen his money and is approaching it. The thief takes the money and runs into the night.

Joseph Your money!

Innkeeper What money? Oh, that money. (*He turns to see it gone.*) My money! My money! Where did it go? My money went away! Oh, I'm such a fool! (*He hits himself repeatedly.*) What will my wife say? She's not one to annoy, Mrs Ezra. Woe is me. Woe!

Mary approaches him.

Mary You were only trying to help us.

Innkeeper Yes, but I wanted to be hard of heart and quick of cunning. Like a panther! Grrrr. Oh, it's no good. I'm not a panther. I'm just a soft moggy! Miaow. Miaow. (*He brushes his head against Mary like a domestic cat.*)

Mary What were you going to say?

Innkeeper That I'm a fat puss!

Mary No, what were you going to say to us?

Innkeeper Hmmn? Oh, just that you could stay in the stable if you like. It's round the back. It's not much, but at least it's covered and I can find some clean straw.

Mary That would be wonderful.

Innkeeper You wouldn't have to pay. I've made so much money tonight anyway.

Pause.

Oh no. I haven't! I haven't! (*He hits himself again.*) Still, you won't pay. Pussycat Ezra is a man of his word. Oh, I shall receive a prize beating for this.

Mary suddenly feels a crumpling pain.

Yes, something like that. Oh, what?

Joseph What is it?

Mary I think it's happening . . . (*She smiles.*)

Innkeeper Oh. Oh. Um. Oh.

Joseph Where is the stable?

Innkeeper Stable?

Joseph The stable!

Innkeeper Oh, *the* stable! I've forgotten.

Mary You said it's round the back.

Innkeeper Yes! It's round the back. Oh my!

Joseph They hurried around the back of the inn. There was a stable, packed with sheep, horses and donkeys.

They go round the back. Some straw falls. It is by no means clean. Animals graze in the stable. Horses. Donkeys.

You mean here?

Innkeeper It's all I've got! Sorry about the smell. Here's some straw. And a blanket.

Joseph It's mouldy.

Innkeeper It's all I've got!

Mary feels another pain.

Mary It's beginning.

Innkeeper Lie down.

Mary I want to sit.

Joseph Have you a milking stool?

Innkeeper Only a bar stool.

Joseph Fetch it. And a saw.

Innkeeper Yes!

> *He does. Joseph expertly turns it into a birth stool.*
> *Mary watches. The animals also. As he works, they*
> *start to make noise, a chorus of animal sounds.*
>   *Mary sits.*

Mary It is happening!

> *Animal music. The animals bay and stamp the ground.*
> *The innkeeper cries and busies himself, running in*
> *circles. Joseph pours water on Mary's head.*

It is happening!

Innkeeper For eight hours she screamed the same words!

Mary It is happening!

Innkeeper The animals bayed and her husband wiped
her face and spoke to her in a soft voice. I fetched water
and food for him and watched this amazing sight!

Mary (*exhausted*) It is happening!

Innkeeper Then suddenly, a remarkable event! The noises
of the town dimmed and became silent. The lights of the
town flickered and extinguished! The world slowed, and
time itself stretched into an eternity! The father fell to
the earth and prostrated himself. The mother gazed
heavenwards. And a light like a river of white fire

poured from the sky into her belly. And I, poor dumb oaf of an innkeeper, fell and worshipped in pure wonder!

The animal music reaches a climax. Then suddenly: silence and stillness. A bright light shines from Mary's belly.
The innkeeper prostrates himself.
Mary stares around her in exhausted awe and wonder.

Mary The world is silent. The world is still. It does not turn. It waits for you.
Be born, child.

The torches above the stable blow out. Darkness.
End of Act One.

Act Two

PROLOGUE

Herod asleep in his royal bed. A storm outside. The linen sheets and silken covers stifle him as he turns and tosses in turbulent dreams . . .

An Attendant That night, King Herod was sleeping in his royal bed . . .

An Attendant In his royal chamber . . .

Another Attendant In his royal palace in Jerusalem . . .

Attendant When a storm broke and Herod was besieged by a terrible dream.

The white sheets rise and stifle Herod as he tosses in sleeping agony.

Herod Aaaaaahhhhhh! Help me! Help me!

Attendants My Lord!

They rush to help him. Herod wakes.

Herod Aaaaah! . . . What? Where am I?

Attendants In your chamber your majesty.
Wake up your majesty.

Minister of Justice You were dreaming my lord.

King Herod I dreamt the land was washed away by an ocean of pure white light. I was drowning, drowning deeper and deeper into darkness . . . I saw a face, the pale face of a child. But I couldn't touch it. A dark cloud came between us. It is an omen. Something is happening . . .

Minister of Justice! Awaken my spies. Find out if a child has been born this night. Wherever it is . . . it must be destroyed!

ONE: BENJAMIN THE SHEPHERD

The crack of thunder, the howling of wind, and the pouring of rain. A hill above Bethlehem. A group of sheep grazing. A huddle of poor clown shepherds shelter under oilskins from the wind and the rain.

Shepherd 1 That night, on a hill above Bethlehem, three poor shepherds were tending their master's sheep.

Shepherd 3 Is it still raining?

Shepherd 2 looks up and is soaked with water.

Shepherd 2 Yup.

Shepherd 3 All our sheep still there?

Shepherds 1 and 2 count the audience.

All still there.

Shepherd 1 (*looking closer at audience*) Ugly bounders aren't they, sheep?

Shepherd 2 But maybe under that woolly exterior they're thinking great thoughts. (*looking closer*) And then again maybe they're not.

Shepherd 3 Weather still not clearing up?

Shepherd 1 looks up. He is soaked too.

Shepherd 1 Nope.

Shepherd 3 That's strange. Twenty minutes ago everything was still as a pond in summer, and now mayhem and chaos.

Shepherd 1 And everyone safe in their homes except for us.

Shepherd 2 Except us.

The howling of a mad animal in the darkness. The shepherds poke their heads out in fright. They are all immediately soaked. The howling starts again.

What was that?

The howling begins again. The shepherds tumble from their oilskins in fear. The third shepherd crosses himself.

Shepherd 1 What is it?

Shepherd 3 It's the beast of the hills.

Shepherd 2 The what?

Shepherd 3 Do you not know the legend of the mad beast that roams the hills at night, killing sheep and eating shepherds alive?

Shepherd 2 No. I didn't know that legend. Did you know about that?

Shepherd 1 No. I hadn't heard about that.

Shepherds 1 and 2 Aaah!

They panic. But Shepherd 3 calms them.

Shepherd 3 Stay calm. The beast only attacks those that move or shake with fear.

The shepherds move and shake with fear.

Shepherd 1 You're shaking!

Shepherd 2 I'm not shaking. He's shaking!

Shepherd 3 I'm not shaking! He's shaking!

And so on until . . .

Shepherd 3 Sssshhh!

The howling comes suddenly nearer.
They back away from the sound and bump into
each other, causing much terror.

Shepherds Aaaaah! Shhhhh!

Shepherd 3 Wait! I've got an idea!

Shepherds 1 and 2 What?

Shepherd 3 We'll hide!

Shepherds 1 and 2 Brilliant!

They try to hide, but there is nothing to hide behind.
They hide behind each other, but it's no good. Now
the howling is quite close. They moan.

Shepherd 3 Wait! I've got an idea.

Shepherds 1 and 2 What?

Shepherd 3 We'll talk to it!

Shepherds 1 and 2 Brilliant! You go first. No, you go
first.

Shepherd 1 Now listen here, beast. You come near our
sheep, we'll kill you with our bare hands!

The beast howls. Shepherd 1 leaps into the arms of
Shepherd 2.

Shepherd 2 Any other brilliant ideas?

Evidently not.

We're going to die.

A mad creature appears, howling.

Shepherd 1 Aaaaah!

Shepherd 2 Aaaaah!

Shepherd 3 Aaaaaah!

They run around in circles. The beast runs around after them. They run away so fast that they end up catching it up by accident and trapping it underneath them.

Shepherd 1 Where is it?

Shepherd 2 Where is it?

Shepherd 3 Where is it?

They feel underneath them.

We've captured the beast of the hills!

Shepherds 1 and 2 We've captured the beast of the hills! Ha ha!

Shepherd 2 We'll be heroes! Ha ha!

Shepherd 1 Quick! Kill it!

Shepherd 2 How?

Shepherd 3 Cut off its head!

Shepherds 1 and 2 Ah ha!

They expose the head of the creature ready to chop it off. It is a man in his early thirties, with a foolish grin and a tragic clown's eyes. It is Benjamin the Shepherd.

Benjamin Baaaoooooow!

Shepherds It's Benjamin the Mad Shepherd!

They cuff him.

Shepherd 2 Benjamin! We thought we'd caught the beast of the hills!

Benjamin I am the beast! Baoooow!

Shepherd 1 I'll teach you to pretend to be a beast! In my house, beasts get the stick taken to them!

He begins to beat Benjamin with his crook. Benjamin leaps around the stage, howling.

Shepherd 3 Leave him now. He's soft in the head, poor fellow. He knows no better.

Benjamin Baaaoooow! I am the beast and I will gobble your children!

Shepherd 2 Yes, we're really scared, Benjamin.

Benjamin I will enter your cottage while you are asleep and eat them all up.

Shepherd 3 Leave him. Mad, he is.

Shepherd 1 There's not one madder. Even his sheep's mad. Look.

One scruffy lunatic sheep enters, baaaing insanely. Benjamin runs to embrace it.

Benjamin My child, my little child.

Shepherd 1 Only got one left. All the rest have died of hunger.

Shepherd 3 I challenge you to find a disease that sheep hasn't got.

Benjamin (*hugging the sheep*) Babe, sweet babe, where did you go?
And your mother so fair, dead of grief.

Shepherd 1 What's he saying?

Shepherd 3 Poor man. It's his wife and child he's ranting about.

Shepherd 2 Benjamin has a wife and child?

Shepherd 3 He did have.

Benjamin Biaoooow! Biaoooow!

Shepherd 3 Benjamin was the finest shepherd in the land. He had the most beautiful wife and the sweetest child you ever could see. Then one day the child was killed by a mad dog on the road. His wife died of grief. And Benjamin started to live like a wild animal. Now he lives nowhere, drinks from puddles, and keeps company only with the trees and the wind.

> *Shepherd 2 starts to cry and is consoled.*
> *Benjamin wrestles himself on the ground.*

Benjamin Baaaooow! (*He leaps up and approaches a sheep.*)

Sheep Baaaa.

Benjamin King Herod! Your majesty, I kiss your feet.

Shepherd 2 It's a sheep you're talking to, Benjamin.

Benjamin King Herod, may I wash your royal feet in the waters of the royal fountain? (*He pisses on the sheep.*) What's that you say, King Herod? You want me to be your prime minister? I thank you, your royal highness. Baaa. (*He kisses the sheep and becomes a sheep prime minister, baaing importantly.*)

Shepherd 3 Calm now, Benjamin.

Benjamin (*seeing them*) Good evening gentlemen. I have been appointed prime minister to the great King Herod. Baaa.

Shepherd 1 You know who we are, Benjamin?

Benjamin Of course. (*to Shepherd 1*) You are my home baaa secretary, you are my foreign baaa secretary and you are my chancellor baaa of the exchequer. Together we rule the land! Home baaa secretary, how are things proceeding?

Shepherd 3 Play along with him, poor fellow.

Shepherd 2 Home baaa affairs are going very well thank you.

Benjamin Excellent. And what news from you chancellor?

Shepherd 1 Only good news.

Benjamin Excellent! Are we baaa taxing enough? I want lots of baaa taxes. For example, are we baaa taxing people who walk like this? (*He walks madly.*)

Shepherds Yes yes, we are.

Benjamin Excellent! (*Benjamin suddenly spies something. He runs over and stares madly at a member of the audience. Then he runs over to the shepherds.*) You know who that is, don't you?

Shepherd 1 It's a sheep, Benjamin.

Benjamin You naive fool. That is a spy. In disguise. He/She's spying on our cabinet meeting, trying to assassinate me. We must arrest him/her immediately.

Benjamin approaches the member of the audience, smiles at him/her falsely, then leaps on him/her. The other shepherds pull him off.

Shepherds Leave him/her alone!

Benjamin (*furious*) He/she's a spy!

Shepherd 3 (*clipping him*) That's enough of your visions now, Benjamin! Enough!

Benjamin (*suddenly cowed*) Biaaaow! Biaaaow!

Shepherd 2 Go to bed, Benjamin!

The thunder cracks. Benjamin howls.

Shepherds Go to bed, mad shepherd! You and your crazy visions!

They retire under their oilskins.
  Alone, Benjamin approaches the lunatic sheep sadly.

Benjamin Bed time, little girl.

Sheep Baaaa. Baaaa.

Benjamin hugs the sheep and is about to lie down when he suddenly sees a star.

Benjamin A star!

The star moves across the sky.

It's moving. It's moving! Wake up! The star's moving! Wake up, wake up! The star is moving!

The shepherds tumble out of their oilskins.

Shepherds What star? What star is moving?

Benjamin There! There!

But it is gone.

Shepherd 3 There'll be no stars in this weather, Benjamin. Go to bed now.

Benjamin I saw it. It moved across the sky . . .

Shepherds You're seeing things.

Benjamin It was there, I swear!

Shepherds Go to bed, Benjamin! Before we get angry. A star that moves! Whatever next?

Benjamin But . . .

The shepherds go back to bed. Benjamin scratches his head.

I'm sure I saw it.

The star appears, but Benjamin does not see it at first.

Or am I mad? Dear God, tell me which it is! (*He looks heavenwards and sees the star.*) The star. The star!

The star moves across the sky.

The star is moving! The star is moving! Wake up! Wake up!

He wakes the other shepherds.

Shepherds What now?

Benjamin The star is there! It's moving!

He points to where it was. But it is no longer there. The shepherds turn on him.

Shepherds You idiot! You try this again, we'll be forced to beat you.

Benjamin But there was a star.

Shepherds There was no star!

Benjamin There was! It moved!

Shepherds There was no star! Say it! There was no star!

Benjamin There was!

They advance on him. He leaps back in fright.

No star! No star!

Shepherds Good. Now get some sleep, and don't interrupt us again.

They return under their covers. Benjamin looks around.

Benjamin There was no star! There was no star, you fool! You idiot! Star indeed! Now I know. I am mad. If I look up I will see it again, because I am mad, and

I will receive a beating. I must look down so as not to see it! (*He throws himself to the ground and buries his face in the earth.*) I will not lift my head until day breaks! Don't look up! Don't look up.

The star appears again. Benjamin remains face down. The sheep sees the star.

Sheep Baaaaa.

Benjamin Quiet, my child. I can't come to you now. I must bury my eyes in the ground so I cannot see.

Sheep Baaaaa. Baaaaa.

Benjamin Oh please be quiet. I cannot come to you.

Sheep Baaaaa. Baaaa. Baaaa. Staaaa. Staaaa. Staaar! Staaar!

Benjamin lifts his head in amazement. Is the sheep really saying 'Staaaar'?
Petrified he looks up at the star. It moves across the sky.

Sheep Staaar!

Sheep and Benjamin Staaar! Staaaar! Staaar! STAAAR!

The other shepherds are woken and leap up.

Shepherds That's it! You've had your warning! You're going to be given a beating you won't forget!

Sheep Staaar.

The shepherds stop in shock.

Shepherd 1 Did that sheep just talk?

Sheep Staaar!

Shepherd 2 Whooooh!

Sheep STAAAR!

They look up. The star moves across the sky.

Shepherds Staaaar!! Staaaar!!

Shepherd 1 It moves! What do we do?

Shepherds Benjamin. What do we do?

Sheep Follow.

Benjamin Follow!

Shepherds Follow!

The shepherds leap up and run after the star.

All Follow!

Shepherds They ran like madmen across fields and over hills, following the bright star in the sky.

Benjamin Benjamin ran ahead and was first to reach the sleeping town. The star came to rest over the stable of a small inn. And there, there . . .

The Angel Gabriel, in beggar form, greets Benjamin.

Who are you?

Gabriel I am the Angel Gabriel.

Benjamin Hello, I'm Benjamin.

Gabriel Benjamin. Ten years ago this night, you lost a child and became mad. Now you will find a new child, and become sane. Because you believed where others had only doubt, you will be first. Come . . .

Benjamin weeps sweet tears of joy and is about to enter when . . .

TWO: THE WISE MEN

Enter Herod and his spies.

Herod In Jerusalem, Herod's spies had been trying to discover something that could explain his horrible dream.

Spy 1 I have searched every town in the region your majesty. There is nothing to report.

Herod Nothing?

Spy 1 Just a bunch of shepherds in Bethlehem yelling about a moving star.

Minister of Justice Don't pay attention to that rabble of low-lifes. They were probably drunk.

Herod Then how can my dream be explained? I must know! All of you, go from my sight and don't come back until you have found what it is that is haunting me!

Spy 2 (*rushes in*) My lord. Three men have arrived in the city. Their feet are bare and all they have for clothes are shirts covered in dirt and holes. They wish to see you.

Herod See me? Worthless tramps. Banish them immediately.

Spy 2 My lord. They claim to be kings from the East.

Herod Kings in rags? What devilish games are being played on me this night?

Minister of Justice They are doubtless confidence tricksters, my lord. I will imprison them forthwith.

Herod Excellent! But how can I be sure?!
  Bring them before me!

Pause. Enter three men in night shirts, soiled and exhausted. Herod laughs.

So you are kings from the East are you?

The entire court laughs contemptuously.

Caspar Not just kings. We are the richest men in the world!

An exotic gong crashes and the kings bow, as Herod watches in horror.

Caspar!

Melchior Melchior!

Balthazar And Balthazar!

Herod Not Balthazar, Caspar and Melchior of Ecbatana?

Balthazar The very same.

Herod But Caspar's mile-long stables of pure Arabian white horses are legendary.
And who has not heard of Melchior's thousand carriages of crusted jewels and rare silks?
And who has not spoken in hushed tones of the white marble palaces of Balthazar?
So what happened? Were you thrown out by murderous revolutionaries, poisoned by your wives, or overthrown by jealous subjects?

Caspar Nothing of the kind.
We all rule over dominions of beauty and plenitude.

Melchior We all have wives of beauty, and children of distinction.

Balthazar And we are all respected as equal in wisdom as in wealth.

Herod So what went wrong!

Melchior We were all bored.

Herod Bored!?

Balthazar Bored.

Caspar Utterly and totally bored.

Melchior Whether playing quoits with diamonds . . .

Caspar Or riding stallions through our infinite lands . . .

Balthazar Or bathing in the pearl-encrusted tubs filled to the brim with yak's milk . . .

Kings Or dining on rare meats and exotic sweets that melted in the mouth. Or ministering to a thousand subjects. Or watching plays and entertainments. Or drinking fine wines. Or being massaged by oils from antique lands. Or or or . . .

Balthazar Life was without meaning.

Melchior And without meaning, life isn't worth living.

Caspar We had only one delight. To meet once a year to compare notes on the night sky.

Balthazar To discuss findings . . .

Melchior And to receive prophecy in the stars.

Herod The stars. What about the stars?

Caspar We had agreed to meet this year in the court of Melchior.

The court.

Balthazar On arrival, we sent away our myriad servants.
Tonight we do not need you.
And proceeded together . . .

Melchior To the vast oak planetarium in the heart of Melchior's palace . . .

Caspar To study the night sky.

The night sky lights up.

The Three Alone at last! No servants! No concubines!

Balthazar Just us and the heavens. This is paradise!

They stare at it in anticipation.

Caspar We waited.

Time passes, literally.

Balthazar We waited.

Time passes again.

Melchior And waited.

Time passes again.

Caspar Nothing happened.

Herod Ha! All fable and fiction!

Melchior Never had the night sky been so dull.

Caspar I have to return to my massive kingdom. Oh misery.

Balthazar I must travel back to my hundred wives. Oh despair.

Melchior Another year of luxurious tedium.
But as we left, we saw that we had not blown out the candle.

Herod Of course not. You have myriad servants for that sort of thing.

Caspar But we've sent them all to bed so we can be alone with the stars.

Herod So wake one up!

Balthazar (*excited*) I've never blown a candle out before.

Caspar It might be enjoyable.

Herod Nonsense!

Melchior But we all want to.

Herod But you are masters of a million subjects! You can't blow out your own candle!

Caspar But we did. All three of us.

> *They blow as one. And immediately a wonderful star appears in the night sky. Darkness below. Heavenly music.*

Herod What is that?

Caspar The star that will lead us to a holy child!

Herod (*horrified*) A child. What child?

> *Herod stares in horror as the star begins to move.*

It moves!

Balthazar It headed west.

Caspar We abandoned our kingdoms . . .

Melchior And pursued it like men possessed across the desert!

Balthazar We took with us gifts for the child!

Caspar I brought forty carriages of gold.

Balthazar And I great vats of frankincense.

Melchior And I several tonnes of myrrh.
We will bow down before this holy king. And life will have meaning!

Men, camels and carriages flood the stage. The journey begins.

Caspar On the journey, disaster befell us!

Balthazar First, ten of our carriages were sent flying over a rock edge and tumbling into an abyss.

Melchior Then, hundreds of servants died of disease.

Caspar Eighty more carriages were lost in a flooded river, taking several hundred servants with them.

Balthazar The rest of the servants fled into the mountains, fearing that the expedition was damned.

Melchior We were alone!

Caspar On our first night, as we slept, our food was stolen by animals.

Balthazar Then we were robbed by brigands, who took the carriage containing the gifts! We had nothing!

Herod So you turned back!

Caspar Back to meaningless luxury?

Melchior Back to abominable money?

Balthazar Back to sterile power? No, we went on! And as we walked naked through the desert, a bird flew over . . .

Melchior And dropped gifts from the sky!

Caspar Into my hand fell a nugget of gold!

Balthazar Into mine a small vial of frankincense.

Melchior And into mine a little pot of myrrh.

Herod But where did they come from?

Balthazar Don't you understand? It was the child's work!

Melchior Suddenly, we felt this soaring happiness envelop us!

Balthazar And we continued on our journey, accompanied only by a wonderful feeling . . .

Caspar Of joy!

Herod A star that moves?! A bird dropping gifts! A child! A child!! What is happening to my mind?

Minister of Justice My lord, these men are clearly insane.

Balthazar The star will lead us to a child. A child that will grow to be the holiest of kings!

Melchior We want to bow down before him and offer him our gifts.

Caspar He is nearby. But we don't know where. Can you help us?

Herod (*suddenly charming*) With pleasure.
   Herod dismissed the kings and summoned his high priests!
   A child has been born this last night. He is destined to be the holiest and mightiest of kings. Holier and mightier than me. I need to know exactly where he is.

Priests The priests studied their holy books. And returned to Herod.
   He will be born in Bethlehem. As it is prophesied in the holy book: 'From Bethlehem shall come a ruler who will govern my people Israel.'

Herod NEVER! NEVER!
   A plan sprouted in the mind of Herod.
   Kings of the East, I hear you wish to worship this new king?

Kings We do.

Herod Then know, it is spoken by the prophecy that you will find him in Bethlehem.

Go. And when you have found him, return immediately and tell me where he lies. I also wish to worship this child. For he will rule over Israel.

Kings Yes, my lord.

They leave.

Herod NEVER!!

Caspar The kings set off for Bethlehem without delay.

Balthazar As night came on, the sky cleared.

Melchior And there was the star once more!

Caspar It came to rest over a tiny dirty stable behind an old ill-kept inn.

Balthazar And there . . .

Caspar There . . .

Melchior There . . .

The scene of the nativity is suddenly revealed. Mary, Joseph and the child attended by Benjamin the shepherd, Ezra the innkeeper and animals.
The kings, whose dress is noticeably similar to that of Benjamin's, bow down in adoration.

Mary You lost everything. Now you have found everything.

Balthazar Never had the kings felt such happiness.

Caspar This is the child we sought.

Melchior It is a miracle!

Caspar That night the kings slept by the mother and baby's side. Although the ground was hard and they had no coverings to protect them from the cold, it was the deepest sleep they had ever slept.

Melchior Their intention was to leave for Jerusalem in the morning to tell King Herod where he could find the child so he too could come to worship him.

Balthazar But that night as they slept, all had the same ominous dream.

> *A crow flies high in the air, swooping over the sleeping Mary and child.*
> *Now hundreds of crows fill the air in a cacophony of vile screaming.*
> *The crows dive down to attack the child. The kings wake up and fight the crows off, screaming.*

Balthazar Take that!

Caspar Get away from here!

Melchior Away from this wondrous child!

> *The crows disappear. The men are left flailing in thin air. Mary and Joseph wake.*

Mary Gentlemen. Wake up.

Balthazar (*waking*) The crows! Where are the crows!

Melchior They were attacking the child!

Mary You were dreaming.

Caspar Dreaming?

Balthazar We dreamt of crows attacking the child.

Melchior What can it mean?

Joseph Joseph remembered Mary's dream when the crow attacked her pregnant belly with its claws.

Kings When did you dream this?

Mary As we approached Jerusalem.

Kings Jerusalem!?

Mary What is it?

Caspar They told the mother and father what had happened in Jerusalem.

Balthazar Of their conversation with Herod and the prophecy of the high priests.

Melchior And how they were due to return there to tell him of the child so he too could come and worship.

Joseph Do not go to him. He is the crow of whom you dreamed. Return home by another route as we came here by another route.

Kings The kings agreed. And avoiding the city of Jerusalem they began the long journey back to their homes.

Mary So, husband, you believe in dreams after all . . .

Herod's palace.

Attendant Herod's palace! The kings were due to return with their news!

Herod The day went by like a slow river. Herod grew angry. Where are those kings? I ordered them to return immediately to me with news of the child.

Minister of Justice It is possible they did not find this child.

Herod You don't believe this child exists, do you?

Minister of Justice My lord. It does seem very unlikely.

Herod Maybe you are right. Moving stars. Birds carrying gifts. Omens! Dreams! All nonsense!
And he laughed a wild hollow cackle of a laugh that was heard through all the corridors of the palace.
Ha ha ha. HA HA HA.

Spy His laugh was interrupted by a spy.
My lord, the three kings from the East have been spied escaping through a remote province back to their own lands.

Herod They have betrayed me! The child does exist! I can feel it. Remember the prophecy. Born to rule over my people Israel! I have been tricked!
(*turning on Minister of Justice*) Who was it who told me to ignore the prophecy? Who laughed at the idea of a moving star, and of kings in rags?

Minister of Justice My lord, please . . .

Herod It was you! You traitor. You would have me ignore these signs so you can take my place! Guards, seize this man! Arrest him, try him fairly, torture and execute him.

Minister of Justice My lord!

Herod Away with him!

The Minister of Justice is seized and taken away screaming.

What do I do now? What do I do?
This child is born to rule over Israel. I could go to worship him, as the kings of the East did. Bow down to one greater than I.
Me worship a child! Impossible! Who is king! Who rules this land!

(*to the spy*) You. Call the commander of my soldiers.

Commander My lord.

Herod You are faithful to me, are you not?

Commander My lord.

Herod Willing to fulfil my every command.

Commander Yes, my lord.

Herod Then listen. There is a child born this last day in Bethlehem. This child is dangerous. He must not live.

Commander Yes, my lord.

Herod Wait. I do not know the exact location of the child.

Commander My lord?

Herod I know he is in Bethlehem, but not where. Tonight you will enter Bethlehem with a thousand men armed with swords and sabres. You will knock on the door of every house and inn. And you will kill the first born of every family. Only then will I know that he is dead.

Commander My lord, there are several thousand people in Bethlehem.

Herod And? Why do you flinch?

Commander But my lord . . .

Herod Did you not vow to be faithful to me in all things?

Commander Yes, my lord.

Herod To fulfil my every command!

Commander Yes, my lord . . .

Herod And now you question me . . .

Commander But my lord . . .

Herod Yes! Your lord! I am your lord! No one but me is your lord!
  Do as I desire. Or pay the consequences.

Commander The commander gathered his forces and gave them their orders.

Herod Herod lingered on the balcony of his palace, waiting for news.

Commander As night fell, the soldiers set off for Bethlehem.

Mary Mary and Joseph had understood the dream well. When Mary was well enough to walk, they began their escape out of Bethlehem.

Soldiers The soldiers invaded the town, armed with swords and sabres.
  The night was black, with not a star in the sky.

  Darkness. A mass entry of soldiers with swords.

Joseph Mary and Joseph were still leaving the town when the soldiers arrived.

Mary They ducked down dark alleyways and hid in shadowy corners.
  Mary clung to her newborn child with all the love in her heart.
  Don't cry, little one.

Joseph The soldiers rushed past on all sides!
  The crunch of boots, the rattle of metal on metal filled their ears!

  The sound of crunching boots and clattering swords overwhelms the stage.

Mary Don't cry, little one!

Soldiers The soldiers began knocking on doors!

The sound of knocking repeated and repeated until it becomes terrifying.

Joseph Now a group of soldiers were right by them.
Joseph and Mary dared not move from their hiding place.

Mary Don't cry, little one!

Joseph They were looking in every hiding hole, sticking sabre points into every dark corner.
They must see us!

The baby cries. The soldiers freeze. A deadly tension.

Soldier Did you hear that? A baby's cry.

Soldier Where's it coming from?

Soldier Here!

Mary The soldier poked his head into the very corner where they were hiding!

Soldier I think there's someone here!
There is!

But when the soldier lays eyes on the child, he freezes, and his voice changes.

No, I was mistaken. There is no one here. (*He falls to the ground.*) Forgive me, my lord. (*The soldier leaps up and runs off.*)

Joseph Run!

Mary They ran as fast as Mary could manage.

Joseph Through narrow streets, across market places, through arches, down alleys, through gates and gardens, until . . .

Mary (*exhausted*) Finally . . .

Joseph They reached freedom!

Soldier But back in the town . . .

The noise reaches a climax.

Soldiers The massacre began! The soldiers tore through the town like a reaper's blade through a field of wheat. Doors were smashed down. Families were ripped apart! Every first-born child was taken from its parents and slain. The crying of mothers and fathers and the screaming of the terrified children as they were led to their deaths echoed through the streets. The town was filled with the sound of pure horror.

A cacophony of noise and screaming grows and grows as the culling takes place. This is the massacre of the innocents.
A strange music intervenes.

But as the killing continued, something miraculous happened. As each innocent life was taken, the soul of the dead child soared above its body and flew into the heavens to become a bright and burning star.

The stars rise.

A night sky of stars, the like of which had never been seen, glistened above Bethlehem.
And the soldiers gazed in wonder at the heavens and said to each other:
Surely this is a miracle.

Herod Herod watched in terror from his balcony in Jerusalem as thousands of stars rose from Bethlehem to settle in the gleaming firmament above him. They looked down on him as the innocent look down on the guilty.

The devil appears.

Herod Who are you?

Devil I am your only friend.

Herod And Herod knew then, as only the devil can know, that he was defeated, and damned to eternal shame.

He flees through the palace corridors, screaming.

Aaaaaaaaaaaaaaah!

The sky of stars makes music of heavenly love as Herod flees in the madness of evil.

EPILOGUE

Joseph and Mary on the road to Egypt.

Joseph Joseph and Mary travelled the long desert road towards the safety of Egypt.
    We will return to our land when times are safe.

Mary The night was calm and still. It reminded Mary of the journey from their home village. She felt they had been travelling forever. Her muscles ached, her bones stung with pain, but her heart sang. She looked at Joseph with a deep love.

Joseph Joseph noticed the look. But said nothing. It was enough.

Mary On their way, they stopped to feed the child.

Joseph They sat on the soft ground.

Mary And looked up at the night sky.

Joseph And as they looked, it seemed they saw their whole story told in the dance of the stars!

Mary and Joseph The marriage!

The annunciation from the beggar angel.
The road to Bethlehem.
Abraham's faith.
David's hope.
Solomon and the magic circle of love.
The dream of the crow.
The madness of the market.
The devil's hotel!
Ezra the innkeeper!
Benjamin the mad shepherd!
The kings: Caspar!
Balthazar!
Melchior!
Herod's madness!
The massacre of the first born.

Mary And high above them the souls of the innocents twinkled like small tears . . .

Joseph Or like jewels!

Mary A breeze rose through the desert trees . . .

Joseph As it had to Joseph that first night when he had doubted Mary's word.

Mary And a word hung on the breeze.

Mary, Joseph and a Choir of Angels Believe!